Violin • Book 3

Terry Shade & Jeremy Woolstenhu

STRING BASICS™
STEPS TO SUCCESS FOR STRING ORCHESTRA

Welcome to **String Basics Book 3**. We are proud that you have entered a new and exciting year in your orchestra program. You will find that **Book 3** has many similarities to **String Basics Books 1** and **2** because it includes a strong mixture of technical studies (left hand and bow arm), as well as a nice selection of classical tunes and melodies representing different cultures from around the world. A variety of duets, chorales, and orchestra arrangements are included to round out the book. Music theory and composition exercises are featured to help you become a well-rounded musician.

As you continue on your journey to becoming a more advanced player, **Book 3** will help you broaden your knowledge of your instrument in many ways; tuning your own instrument, shifting, learning advanced time signatures and key signatures, playing more difficult rhythms, harmonics, trills, and grace notes. You will also begin the initial steps toward learning vibrato!

If you have been practicing with a metronome up to this point, congratulations! Continue working with your metronome throughout **Book 3** as it will be beneficial. If you are new to working with a metronome, now is the perfect time to include it into your daily practice routine. Using a metronome is one of many steps to take toward becoming a strong and successful musician.

Best wishes,

Terry Shade

Jeremy Woolstenhulme

String Basics is available in SmartMusic.
To subscribe, go to www.smartmusic.com.

smartmusic®

ISBN-10: 0-8497-3514-9 • ISBN-13: 978-0-8497-3514-1

©2013 Kjos Music Press, Neil A. Kjos Music Company, Distributor, 4382 Jutland Drive, San Diego, California, 92117.

Tuning Your Violin: Small Adjustments

Before beginning the tuning process, take a look at the pegs & peg box, the tailpiece & fine tuners, and the bridge. In the photos here, notice how the strings cleanly wrap around the pegs. Examine which strings wrap around which pegs. Also examine the tailpiece and fine tuners. Which strings have fine tuners? Finally, take a close look at the strings where they nestle into the grooves of the crown (top of the bridge).

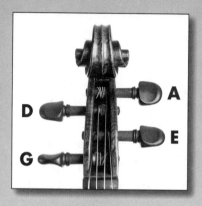

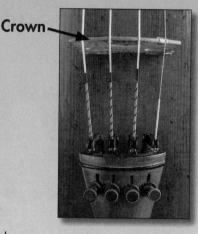

Crown

To begin, have a reference pitch that can sustain a continuous tone. Start with A-440. Listen to the A pitch and ask yourself: Is my A higher or lower, or in tune (identical) to the given A? You may also want to use a needle or dial tuner. These tuners indicate when the string is flat or sharp depending on what the needle is telling you. If the needle is lined up with the note, then the string is in tune. Make sure the tuner is calibrated to 440, unless directed otherwise.

Tuning With Fine Tuners (Pizzicato)

• Sit in a chair with your violin facing you.

• Listen closely to the A given from your reference pitch.

• Pluck your A string repeatedly with your left thumb while turning the fine tuner with the other hand.

• Decide whether to turn the fine tuner clockwise (to raise the pitch) or counterclockwise (to lower the pitch).

• Work towards matching the two pitches perfectly.

• Tune the rest of your strings in this order: D, G, E. Adjust the tuning device for each of these pitches.

Tuning With Fine Tuners (Arco)

• Place your bow at the tip and play your A very softly (so that you can also hear the tuning device pitch).

• Touch your fine tuner by reaching underneath your violin with your left arm.

• Turn the fine tuner clockwise to raise the pitch of your string or turn it counterclockwise to lower the pitch.

• Work towards matching the pitches perfectly. It may be necessary to tilt your head to your left to better hear yourself.

• Tune your remaining strings using double stops in this order: AD, DG, EA.

Tuning Your Violin: Large Adjustments

Tuning With Pegs (Pizzicato)

• Use the pegs only if any one or more of your strings are loose (slack), extremely out of tune, or if you don't have fine tuners installed for all four strings. When first learning to use pegs, tune sitting in a chair, with your violin facing you.

• Begin by turning the peg toward you as little as possible to slightly loosen the tension of the string. Do this before attempting to actually match the pitch from the tuner.

• Pluck the string repeatedly with your left thumb while positioning your right hand on the peg.

• Push the peg in toward the peg box as you turn it toward the scroll. Turn the peg just a little at a time so the string doesn't accidentally break.

• Turn the peg slightly forward to raise the pitch of the string and turn the peg toward you to lower the pitch. Use the peg to match the given pitch as accurately as possible. If you have a fine tuner on the string, make final, tiny adjustments to complete the process.

Tuning With Pegs (Arco)

• For more accurate tuning, have your bow already placed on the string when beginning the tuning process.

• Grip the correct peg by placing your thumb on one side of the peg and your 1st and 2nd fingers on the opposite side of the peg (see closeup photo below). This finger positioning will help you press the peg into the peg box while turning it at the same time.

• If the peg is too difficult to turn, you may want to loosen the peg by pulling it out and turning it a bit (counter clockwise).

• Make very small "click turns" with the peg. A slight turn can make a big difference in the pitch. Turning the peg excessively could cause the string to break!

• Continuously execute small turns that are slightly lower, then slightly higher than the given pitch. As you are "closing in" on the correct pitch, rock your peg back and forth until the string is in tune.

Successful Tuning Tips

1. Use your fine tuners as much as possible. If a fine tuner become screwed all the way in, loosen it most of the way out (turning counterclockwise) before carefully tightening the peg to reach the necessary pitch.

2. Ask your teacher for help if your fine tuners are too stiff and difficult to turn, or if your pegs simply won't budge.

3. If your instrument is severely out of tune to begin with, you will probably need to retune it several times.

4. If a string has become loose, be sure that the string is sitting in the groove on the crown of the bridge *before* tightening it with the peg.

5. When tuning your strings in orchestra class, play softly.

6. Learning to tune your own instrument is an ongoing process and it takes practice, patience, and some skills. Quite simply, the more you do it, the easier it becomes!

Review: D & G Major, A & D Minor

Steps to Success:
❑ Establish group pulse
❑ Play with good intonation and tone

1. D Major

2. G Major

3. A Minor

4. D Minor

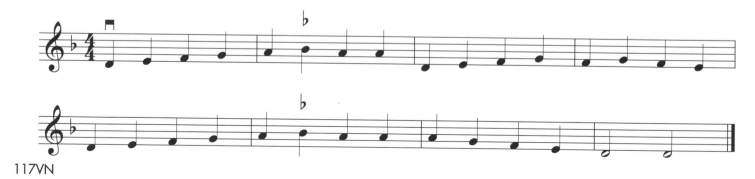

Steps to Success:
- ❑ Hold bow correctly
- ❑ Play using three different bow arm levels

A string level

D string level

G string level

5. Open String Slurs

6. Separate Crossings

7. Careful Bowings

8. Three String Slur

9. The Swift Up Bow

10. All About the Bow

rit.

6 Review: Finger Patterns

Steps to Success:
- ❏ Play D Major 2-3 finger pattern
- ❏ Play D Minor 1-2 finger pattern
- ❏ Play G Minor 1-2 finger pattern

2-3 finger pattern

1-2 finger pattern

11. D to A in D Major

12. Musette

Johann Sebastian Bach (1685–1750)
German Composer

13. D to A in D Minor

14. Minuet TEST LINE

Johann Sebastian Bach (1685–1750)
German Composer

15. Pat-A-Pan

French Carol

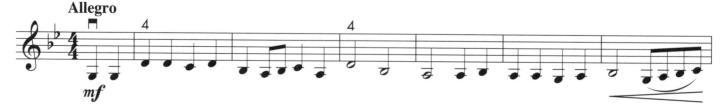

Review: Low 1st Finger

Steps to Success:
- ❑ Identify half steps and whole steps
- ❑ Play open finger pattern
- ❑ Play "low" 3-4 finger pattern
- ❑ Understand and play *a tempo*
- ❑ Identify major and minor key signatures

open pattern

low 3-4 finger pattern

a tempo = return to the original tempo after a *ritard.* or a fermata

16. Open Pattern

17. Challenger Deep

18. B♭ to E♭ in B♭ Major

19. The Rakes of Mallow

Irish Folk Song

20. Steps to Learning Theory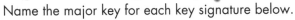

Name the major key for each key signature below.

Review: High 3rd Finger (Violin, Viola)/Forward Extension (Cello)

Steps to Success:
- ❏ Play 3-4 finger pattern on the G string
- ❏ Play staccato

3-4 finger pattern on G string

21. The C♯ Stretch – *Duet*

22. Now Is the Month of Maying

Thomas Morley (1559–1602)
English Composer

23. Theme from "Serenade for Strings"

Peter Ilyich Tchaikovsky (1840–1893)
Russian Composer

24. Coventry Carol

English Carol

Steps to Success:

❏ Identify and play Louré bowing

❏ Understand **Adagio**

Louré = long hooked legato notes with the bow. There is slight separation between the slurred notes.

Adagio = slow tempo, slower than **Andante**

25. Louré – *Quartet*

26. Las Mañanitas

Mexican Folk Song

27. Danny Boy

Irish Folk Song

Steps to Success:
- ❑ Place high 3rd finger on G#
- ❑ Understand A Major key signature
- ❑ Play A Major Scale

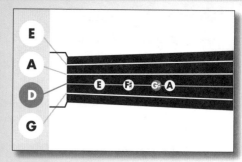

G#: high 3rd finger on D string

A Major = = 3 sharps: F#, C#, G#.

28. Going for G# – *Duet*

29. Let's Take Turns

Andante

Everyone   *Cello/Bass*   *Viola*   *Violin*

30. A Major Scale – *Memorization Line*

31. Sicilian Hymn

Traditional

Moderato

32. Bella Bimba

Italian Folk Song

Allegro

Steps to Success:
- ❑ Place high 2nd finger on G♯
- ❑ Play upper octave A Major Scale

G♯: 2nd finger on E string

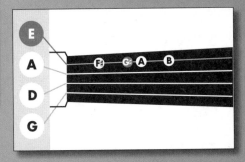

33. G♯ on E String – *New Step for Violin and Bass*

34. Upper Octave A Major Scale – *New Step for Violin*

35. Chester

William Billings (1746–1800)
American Composer

36. Gentle Mother

Japanese Folk Song

37. Minuet

Alexander Reinagle (1756–1809)
American Composer

Steps to Success:

❏ Play sixteenth notes

❏ Play eighth & sixteenth note combinations

❏ Play near the bridge and use less bow

38. Sixteenth and Eighth Notes Reunion – *Trio*

Use less bow and play close to the bridge.

39. Rhythmic Scale in G Major – *Steps to Learning Theory*

Write in the counts before playing.

40. Sourwood Mountain

American Folk Song

Moderato

mf   *f*

41. Cripple Creek

American Folk Song

Allegro

f   *p*

f

42. B♭ Major Scale in 92 Notes!

43. Tirra Lirra Loo

Canadian Folk Song

Moderato   *Fine*   *D.C. al Fine*

f   *p*   *mf*

44. A Major Broken Thirds and Arpeggio

45. When I Was a Lad from "H.M.S. Pinafore"

Sir Arthur Sullivan (1843–1900)
English Composer

Allegro

f

46. Steps to Learning Theory

3/4

Complete each measure using these notes: ♫♫♫ ♫♫ ♫♫. Check the time signature. Write in the counting and perform your new rhythm line on open D.

Steps to Success:

❏ Understand **Andantino**

> **Andantino** = a tempo slightly faster than **Andante** and slower than **Moderato**

> **sim.** = **simile** = continue playing in the same way

47. Dance – *Duet*

Daniel Gottlob Türk (1750–1813)
German Composer

48. Theme from "William Tell Overture" – *Orchestra Arrangement*

Gioacchino Rossini (1792–1868)
Italian Composer

Dotted Eighth & Sixteenth Note Combinations

Steps to Success:
- ❏ Count and play dotted eighth & sixteenth note combinations
- ❏ Play dotted rhythms using hooked bowings
- ❏ Play dotted rhythms using slurs
- ❏ Understand *D.S. al Coda*

Dotted Eighth & Sixteenth Note Combination = ♪. ♬ = 1 beat

D.S. al Coda (Dal Segno al Coda) = go back to the sign 𝄋 and play until reaching *"To Coda ⊕,"* then jump to the Coda.

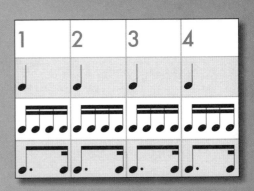

49. Dotted Eighth & Sixteenth Drill – *Duet*

1 e & a 2   a 3 e & a 4   a 1 e & a 2   a 3 e & a 4   &

50. Barnyard – *Duet*

51. Battle Cry of Freedom

George F. Root (1825–1895)
American Composer

117VN

52. The Golden Hook

53. Bridal Chorus from "Lohengrin"

Richard Wagner (1813–1883)
German Composer

54. Battle Hymn of the Republic

American Civil War Hymn

55. Hey, Ho, Nobody Home – *Round*   TEST LINE

English Carol

56. Theme from Symphony No. 8 "Unfinished"

Franz Schubert (1797–1828)
Austrian Composer

Chromatic Scale

Steps to Success:
- ❏ Understand and play chromatic melodies
- ❏ Play C chromatic scale

> Chromatic Scale = a series of 12 ascending or descending half steps

57. Chromatic Scale Prep

58. Chromatic Study

59. C Chromatic Scale

60. Habanera

Georges Bizet (1838–1875)
French Composer

Katie Carlson

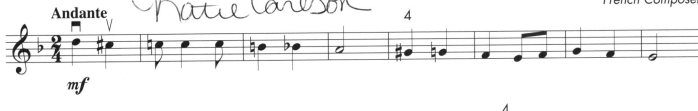

61. La Cumparsita – *Orchestra Arrangement*

Gerardo H. Matos Rodríguez (1897–1948)
Uruguayan Composer

Steps to Success:

❏ Execute correct sliding motion of shifting to 3rd position

❏ Play with proper left hand shape

❏ Identify 1st and 3rd position according to given fingerings

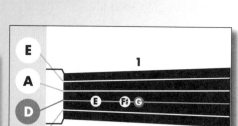
Video Lesson #2

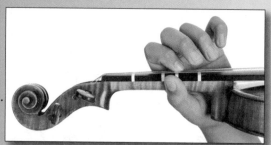

Shift to G: Slide 1st finger on the D string towards the bridge. The hand, including the thumb, moves as a unit.

62. Shifting to 3rd Position – *Duet*

63. Totally in 3rd Position

64. Sliding to G with First Finger

65. Sliding to D with First Finger

Steps to Success:
- ❏ Understand fingerings and notes in 3rd position on D & A strings
- ❏ Identify and play the correct finger pattern in 3rd position
- ❏ Play G Major Scale in 3rd position

3–4 pattern on A string
in 3rd position

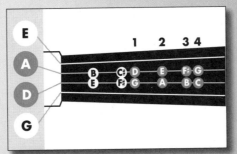

Posture for 3rd position

66. Heading Up on D and A Strings

67. Cellists Go to the 4th

68. Reaching for the Stars

69. Autumn from "The Four Seasons"

Antonio Vivaldi (1678–1741)
Italian Composer

70. G Major Scale in Position – *Memorization line*

Same Finger Shifting (Ascending and Descending)

Steps to Success:
- ❏ Play shifts using 1st finger
- ❏ Play shifts using 2nd finger
- ❏ Execute correct sliding motion of shifting (up and back) with left hand
- ❏ Identify left hand position according to given fingerings

71. Sliding Between 1st & 3rd Positions

72. Sliding Along

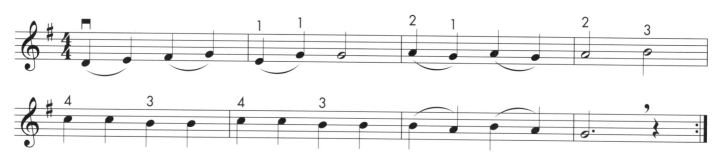

73. The Sugar Glider – *Duet*

74. Fleeting Years

75. Oh! Susanna

Stephen Foster (1826–1864)
American Composer

Steps to Success:
❏ Understand modulation

> Modulation = changing from one key to another

76. Extended 3rd Position for Cello

77. At Pierrot's Door – *Duet – New Step for Bass*

French Folk Song

78. Ye Banks and Braes o' Bonnie Doon

Scottish Folk Song

79. Mo Li Hua [Beautiful Jasmine Flower]

Chinese Folk Song

Steps to Success:
- ❏ Understand and play correct fingerings for given intervals
- ❏ Play on correct string according to given fingerings
- ❏ Play in position with good tone and accurate rhythm

80. Rainbow Vista

81. Petroglyphs

Moderato

82. Waltz of the White Domes

Andante

83. The Old Brass Wagon – *Duet*

American Folk Song

Moderato

84. The Technician's Overhaul

85. The Roly Poly Water Drops – *Duet*

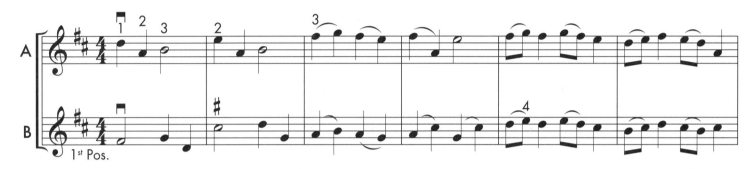

86. Camptown Races

Stephen Foster (1826–1864)
American Composer

87. March from "Scipio"   TEST LINE

George Frideric Handel (1685–1759)
English Composer

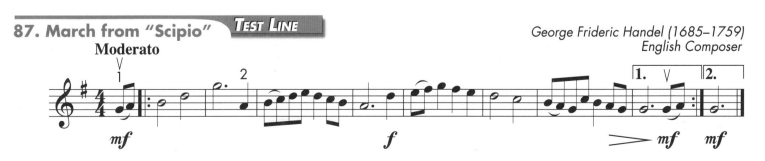

Natural Harmonics/Glissando to Harmonics

Steps to Success:

❏ Play harmonics on each string with proper technique and posture

❏ Play glissando up to natural harmonic

Glissando = gliding or sliding from one note to another

Natural Harmonic = special flute-like tones created by lightly touching the string at the mid-point

harmonics hand posture

88. Harmonics

Lightly touch the string with the 4ᵗʰ finger.

89. Going the Octave with Harmonics

90. Glissando Road

Start each measure in 1ˢᵗ position.

91. Shifting to Harmonics

92. Harmonic Waltz – *Duet*

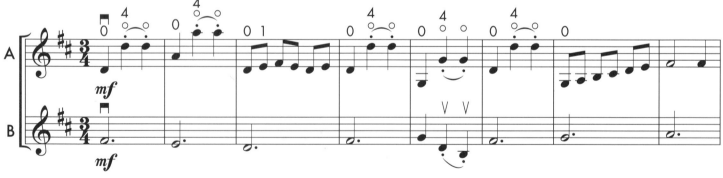

Steps to Success:

- ❏ Play A-B-C#-D on the E String
- ❏ Play 3-4 finger pattern in 3rd position
- ❏ Play upper octave D Major Scale

3–4 pattern on E string

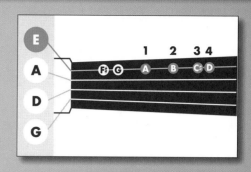

93. Up to Harmonic G

94. G Major Scale

95. Up to the Stratosphere – *New Step for Violin*

96. D Major Scale – *New Step for Violin – Duet*

97. John Peel

English Folk Song

117VN

Shape Shifter
for String Orchestra

Jeremy Woolstenhulme (b.1974)
American Composer

(stay in 3rd position)

Steps to Success:

❑ Count and play eighth note triplets

❑ Identify and play bow retrievals

| Eighth Note Triplet = ♪♪♪ (3) = ♩ = 1 beat |
| Bow Retrieval = (V) = technique used when needing to bring the bow back near the frog so that you can play a short up bow stroke. |

98. Playing Triplets

Name the scale featured in this exercise. _____

99. Three in One

100. Triplet Scale – *Memorization line*

101. Theme from "Zampa"

Ferdinand Hérold (1791–1833)
French Composer

102. Triumphal March from "Aida"

Giuseppe Verdi (1813–1901)
Italian Composer

Slow $\frac{6}{8}$ Time (Counting in 6)

Steps to Success:
- ❏ Play and count $\frac{6}{8}$ time (slow tempo)
- ❏ Conduct slow tempo $\frac{6}{8}$ pattern

Time Signature (Slow) = $\frac{6}{8}$ $\frac{6}{8}$ = beats per measure
$\frac{6}{8}$ = ♪ receives 1 beat

Conducting Pattern = = A 6-beat pattern

103. Slow $\frac{6}{8}$

104. Scale in $\frac{6}{8}$

105. Quarters & Eighths

106. Romanza from Sonatina

Ludwig van Beethoven (1770–1827)
German Composer

Andantino

mp

107. Sumer Is Icumen In – *Steps to Learning Theory*

13th Century English Folk Song

Draw in the barlines, then play.

Steps to Success:
❑ Play and count $\frac{6}{8}$ time (fast tempo)
❑ Play slurs and hooked bowings in $\frac{6}{8}$ time
❑ Play and understand **Presto**

Presto = very fast, faster than **Allegro**

Time Signature (Fast) = $\frac{6}{8}$ = 2 beats per measure
= ♩. receives 1 beat

Conducting Pattern = = A 2-beat pattern

1	la	le	2	la	le

108. Irish Washerwoman

Irish Folk Song

Presto

109. Slurring in $\frac{6}{8}$ Time

110. Name the Major or Minor Key

TEST LINE

111. Row Your Boat – Round

Traditional

Allegro

112. Barcarolle from "The Tales of Hoffmann"

Jacques Offenbach (1819–1880)
French Composer

Andante

To Coda

D.C. al Coda

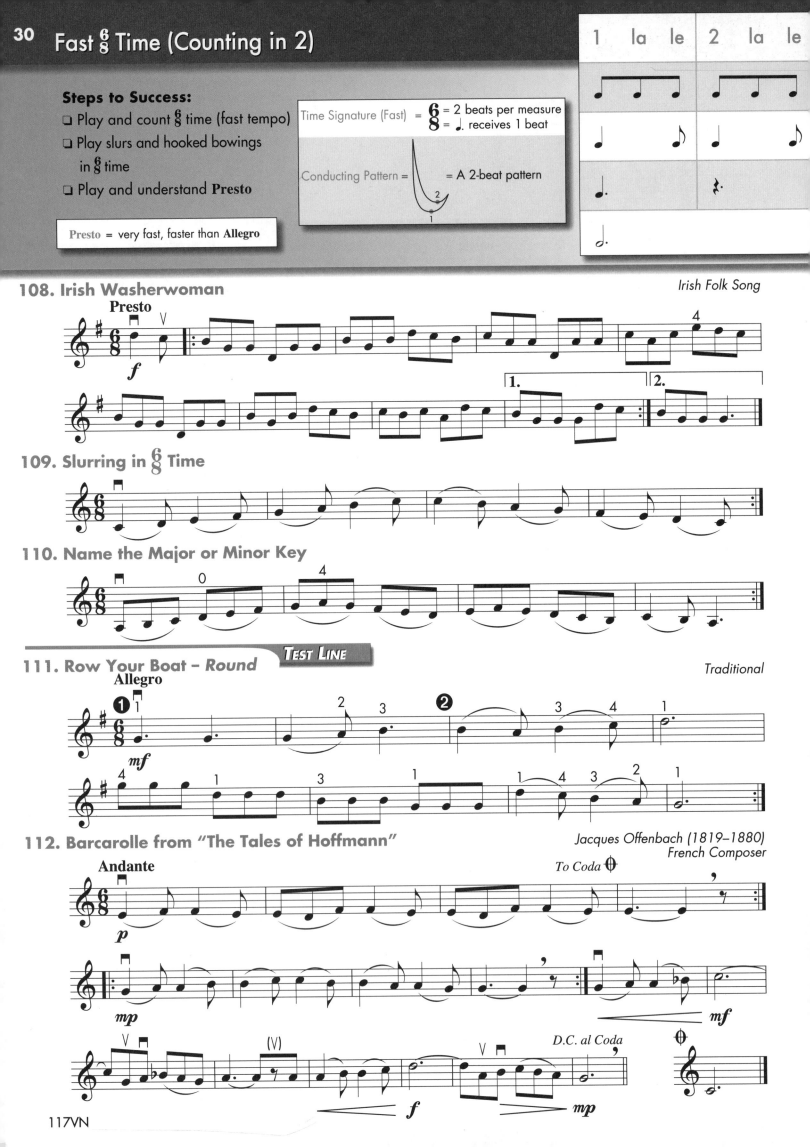

117VN

13. Theme from "Capriccio Italien"

Peter Ilyich Tchaikovsky (1840–1893)
Russian Composer

14. Greensleeves

English Folk Song

15. I Saw Three Ships

English Carol

16. I'se the B'y that Builds the Boat

Canadian Folk Song

Gigue

from *Orchestral Suite No. 3*
for *String Orchestra*

Johann Sebastian Bach (1685–1750)
German Composer
arr. Jeremy Woolstenhulme

32

$\frac{9}{8}$ & $\frac{12}{8}$ Time

Steps to Success:

❑ Count and play in compound meters of $\frac{9}{8}$ and $\frac{12}{8}$ time

❑ Play in compound meters with correct notes and bowings

Cantabile = to play lyrically, in a singing style

117. Three Groups of Three

118. Theme from Cello Concerto, Op. 85

Edward Elgar (1857–1934)
English Composer

119. Four Groups of Three

120. Andante Cantabile from Symphony No. 5

Peter Ilyich Tchaikovsky (1840–1893)
Russian Composer

Steps to Success:
- ❏ Play 3rd position in D Minor with 2-3 finger pattern
- ❏ Understand half and whole steps in D Minor

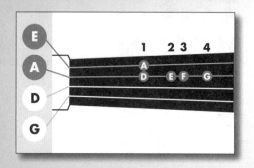

2-3 finger pattern in 3rd position

121. Finding D Minor in 3rd Position

122. Theme from Symphony No. 1

Gustav Mahler (1860–1911)
Austrian Composer

123. Spinning a Web

124. Rigaudon – *Duet*

Georg Philipp Telemann (1681–1767)
German Composer

3rd Position: Mixed Finger Patterns (Violin)

Steps to Success:

❏ Play 2-3 finger pattern on E string and 3-4 pattern on A string
❏ Use bow retrieval to accomplish good bow usage

2-3 finger pattern in 3rd position

3-4 finger pattern in 3rd position

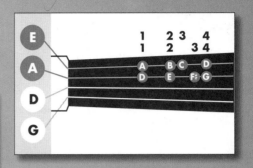

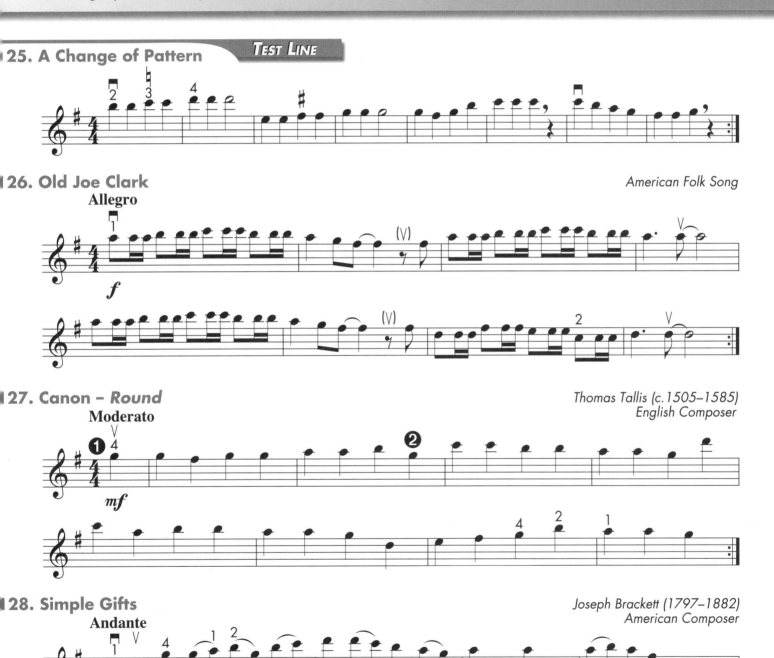

25. A Change of Pattern   *TEST LINE*

26. Old Joe Clark   *American Folk Song*

Allegro

27. Canon – *Round*   *Thomas Tallis (c.1505–1585)*
English Composer

Moderato

28. Simple Gifts   *Joseph Brackett (1797–1882)*
American Composer

Andante

rit.

Steps to Success:
- Understand fingerings in 2nd position
- Play correct finger patterns in 2nd position

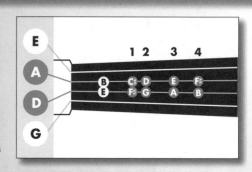

2nd position on A string with 1st finger on C#

129. Shifting to 2nd Position

130. Sliding Into Second

131. Second Nature – *Duet*

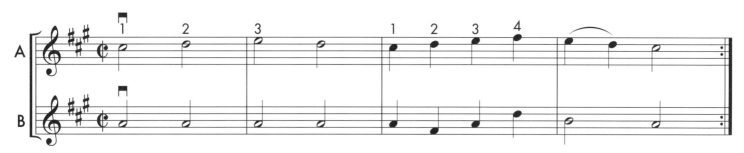

132. Second Time Around – *Duet*

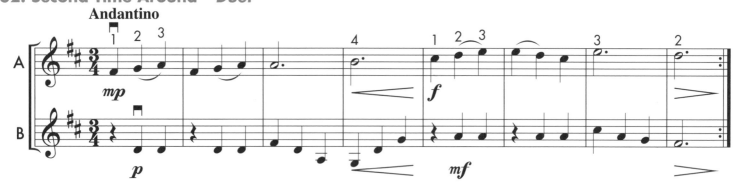

133. Playing Until the Last Second – *Duet*

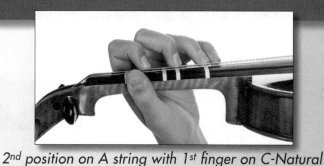

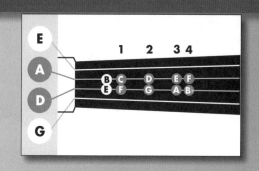

2nd position on A string with 1st finger on C-Natural

34. Extended Hand Position

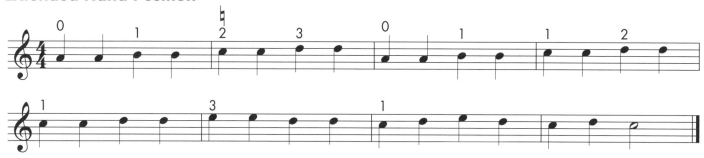

35. First Finger Glider – *Duet*   **TEST LINE**

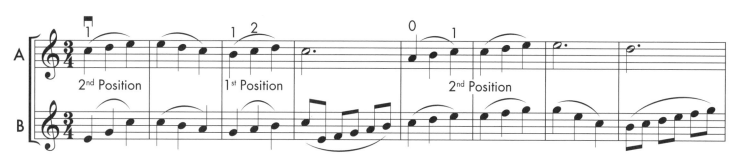

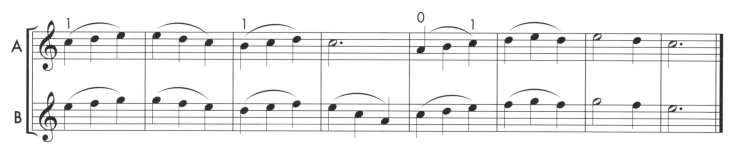

36. Chico de Chile

37. Country Dance Party – *Duet*

117VN

Steps to Success:
- Understand Eb Major key signature
- Play low 3-4 finger pattern on the D string
- Play in Eb Major in 2nd position

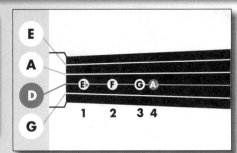

low 3-4 finger pattern on D string

Eb Major = 3 flats: Bb, Eb, Ab.

138. Adding Ab – *Duet*

139. Ab New Octave

140. Eb Major Scale

141. Theme from Symphony No. 5

Ludwig van Beethoven (1770–1827)
German Composer

142. Ach, Du Lieber Augustin

German Folk Song

Steps to Success:
- ❏ Play 1-2 finger pattern on the A and E strings
- ❏ Play in Eb Major in 1st and 3rd positions
- ❏ Understand half steps in Eb Major

1-2 finger pattern in 3rd position

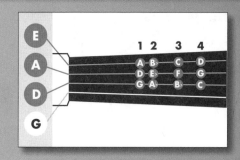

43. March in _____ Major

Fill in the blank above and mark the half steps.

44. Fresh Rain – Duet   **TEST LINE**

Andante

45. Child's Play

Moderato

46. Tingalayo   *Caribbean Folk Song*

Moderato

Steps to Success:

❑ Understand E Major key signature

❑ Play 3-4 finger pattern on the A string

❑ Play in ½ position on the D string

❑ Play E Major scale

½ position on D string

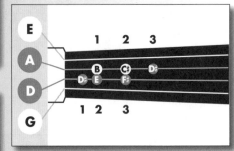

E Major = = 4 sharps: F#, C#, G#, D#.

147. Adding D♯ – *Duet*

148. E Major Scale

149. E Major Broken Thirds

150. Willkommen, lieber schöner Mai, D. 244 – *Round*

Franz Schubert (1797–1828)
Austrian Composer

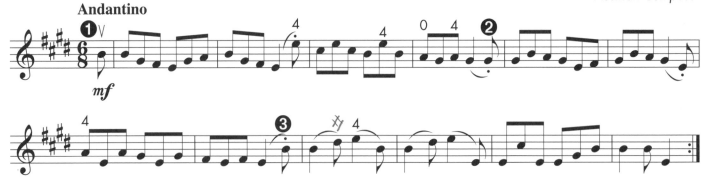

151. ½ Position is Great!

152. The Mulberry Bush *English Folk Song*

153. Allegro from String Quartet No. 4, K. 157 *Wolfgang Amadeus Mozart (1756–1791) Austrian Composer*

154. The Glendy Burke Practice this line on an open string first to learn the rhythm. *Stephen Foster (1826–1864) American Composer*

155. The British Grenadiers *English Folk Song*

156. Steps to Learning Theory

Add accidentals to play the melody in E Major.

Steps to Success:

❏ Identify differences between natural, melodic & harmonic minor scales in different keys
❏ Play natural, melodic & harmonic minor scales in different keys

Natural Minor Scale	= Half steps occur between the 2ⁿᵈ & 3ʳᵈ and 5ᵗʰ & 6ᵗʰ notes of the scale. *See #157.*
Harmonic Minor Scale	= This is similar to a natural minor scale except that the 7ᵗʰ note is raised a half step. *See #158.*
Melodic Minor Scale	= When ascending, the 6ᵗʰ and 7ᵗʰ notes (of the natural minor scale) are raised a half step, and when descending, the notes are the same as the natural minor scale. *See #159.*

157. D Natural Minor Scale

158. D Harmonic Minor Scale

159. D Melodic Minor Scale

160. G _____ Minor Scale – *Steps to Learning Theory*

Write the name of this minor scale on the line above.

161. E Melodic Minor Scale – *Steps to Learning Theory*

Add the appropriate accidentals to make this a Melodic Minor scale.

162. C Melodic Minor Scale

163. C Harmonic Minor Scale – *Steps to Learning Theory*

Write a one-octave scale reflecting the title. Use quarter notes as in 157.

164. Joshua Fought the Battle at Jericho

American Spiritual

165. March Slav – *Orchestra Arrangement*

Peter Ilyich Tchaikovsky (1840–1893)
Russian Composer

166. Chorale in E Minor – *Orchestra Arrangement*

Johann Sebastian Bach (1685–1750)
German Composer

Steps to Success:

❏ Understand grace note notation
❏ Play grace notes
❏ Play spiccato at a fast tempo

Grace Note = = an ornamental note printed in small type

167. The Gypsy Baron Overture

Johann Strauss, Jr. (1825–1899)
Austrian Composer

168. Turkish March from "Six Variations for Piano, Op. 76"

Ludwig van Beethoven (1770–1827)
German Composer

169. Spiccato in B Minor

170. It's All About the Bowings

171. Can Can from "Orpheus in the Underworld" – Duet

Jacques Offenbach (1819–1880)
French Composer

172. Steps to Learning Theory

Name the major key for each key signature below.

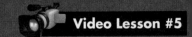

Vibrato = a pulsating effect made by repeatedly rolling the pressed fingertip slightly forward and backward and is generated by the left hand/arm. Because the finger moves forward and backward so quickly, the pitch varies slightly to create vibrato. Vibrato produces an expressive and warm tone and adds intensity and depth to your playing.

For violinists and violists, there are two primary types of vibrato:

1) Arm vibrato – moving the arm at the elbow to achieve the pulsating effect

2) Wrist vibrato – moving the wrist to achieve the pulsating effect

❑ The left hand, arm, and shoulder must be relaxed. Tension throughout your body will make vibrato nearly impossible to achieve.

❑ The thumb should not be squeezing the neck of the instrument.

❑ You will only have two contact points with the instrument: left hand thumb and finger.

❑ The first finger knuckle (across from the thumb) should have a slight space from the neck to allow for proper vibrato movement.

Finger Slides F→E→F (♩ = 72)

These finger slides will look like you are polishing your string. Try these exercises without the bow first, then add the bow once you have correctly accomplished the slides.

REMINDER: Your thumb should be relaxed and flexible, and the pad of the thumb should rock with the sliding motion, however it will stay in one place.

Finger Slides G→F♯→G (♩ = 72)

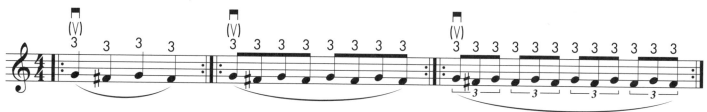

Finger Slides E→D♯→E (♩ = 72)

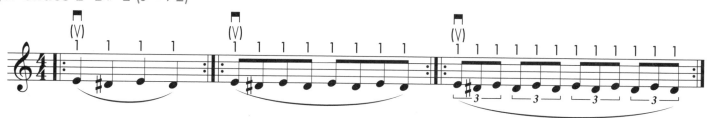

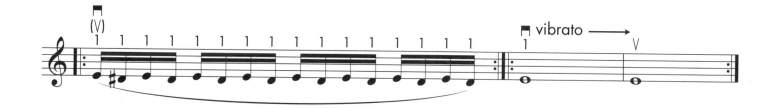

Finger Slides A→G♯→A (♩ = 72)

Glossary

a tempo *(7)*

Return to the original tempo after a **ritard.** or a fermata.

Adagio *(9)* [Italian]

One of the slowest tempo marks in music, slower than **Andante**.

Andantino *(14)* [Italian]

A tempo mark indicating a speed slightly faster than **Andante** and slower than **Moderato**.

Arpeggio *(13)* [Italian]

A series of notes which make up the 1st, 3rd, 5th, and 8th notes of the scale.

Bow Retrieval *(28)*

Technique used when needing to bring the bow back near the frog so that a short eighth note up bow (V) stroke can be played.

Cantabile *(33)* [Italian]

To play lyrically, in a singing style.

Chromatic Scale *(17)*

A series of 12 ascending or descending half steps.

D.S. al Coda (Dal Segno al Coda) *(15)* [Italian]

Go back to the sign and play until reaching "To Coda," then jump to the Coda.

Eighth Note Triplet *(28)*

 = 1 beat

Glissando *(24)* [Italian]

A continuous sliding of pitch from one note to another. It can be used as a special effect.

Grace Note *(44)*

An ornamental note printed in small type.

Harmonic (Natural) *(24)*

Special flute-like tones created by lightly touching the string at specific locations along the fingerboard. Harmonic notes are notated with a small o and a 4.

Key Signatures

A Major *(10)*

B♭ Major/g minor

C Major/a minor

D Major/b minor

E Major *(40)*

E♭ Major/c minor *(38/42)*

F Major/d minor

G Major/e minor

Louré *(9)* [French]

A style of bowing featuring long hooked legato notes. There is slight separation between the notes.

Minor Scales *(42)*

A series of eight notes in a particular stepwise ascending and descending order with a specific pattern of whole steps and half steps. There are three forms of the minor scale:

Harmonic Minor Scale

Half steps occur between the 2nd and 3rd, and 5th and 6th notes of the scale. The 7th note is raised a half step.

Melodic Minor Scale

When ascending, the 6th and 7th notes of the natural minor scale are raised a half step, and when descending, the notes are the same as the natural minor scale.

Natural Minor Scale

Half steps occur between the 2nd and 3rd, and 5th and 6th notes of the scale.

Modulation *(21)*

Changing from one key to another within a composition.

9/8 Time *(33)*

3 beats per measure and a dotted quarter note receives one beat. The conducting pattern for 9/8 time is:

Presto *(30)* [Italian]

A tempo mark indicating very fast, faster than **Allegro**.

Shifting *(18)*

A sliding or gliding motion with the left hand and arm to move from one position to another.

Simile or sim. *(14)* [Italian]

Continue playing in the same way such as with articulations and/or bowings.

6/8 Time (Fast: Counting in Two) *(30)*

2 beats per measure and a dotted quarter note receives one beat. The conducting pattern for fast 6/8 is:

6/8 Time (Slow: Counting in Six) *(29)*

6 beats per measure and an eighth note receives one beat. The conducting pattern for slow 6/8 is:

12/8 Time *(33)*

4 beats per measure and a dotted quarter note receives one beat. The conducting pattern for 12/8 is:

Vibrato *(46)*

A technique that produces an expressive and warm sound made by the pulsating effect generated by the left hand and arm.